THE PIED PIPER

CHARACTERS
Pied Piper
Mayor
Woman with basket
Man with hat
Woman with baby
Cook
Women with brushes
Lame Boy
Children
Rats

Retold by Ann Wade
Illustrated by Holly Swain

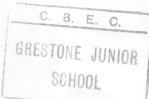

Collins Educational
An Imprint of HarperCollinsPublishers

On stage, one or two people are talking to the Mayor.
They seem angry. Screams from offstage.
In runs a woman with a basket, shouting loudly.

Woman with basket: Rats! Rats!

Man with hat: *(runs in holding his hat)* Rats in my hat!

Woman with baby: *(rushes in)* Rats in my baby's cot!

Cook: *(waving a big spoon)* Rats in my chocolate cake!

Women with brushes: *(they run in, shouting)* Rats! Rats running in our kitchens. Rats squeaking under our chairs. Rats peeping out of our cupboards. Rats scurrying under our beds.

Woman with basket: *(pleading)* Mr. Mayor, you must help us.

Mayor: But what can I do?

Man with hat: You're the Mayor – you must do *something*!

Mayor: But I've tried *everything*. I can't get rid of them.

Cook: *(determined)* Then you must go. You're no use if you can't help us.

All: Yes, Yes. *(Everyone starts talking at once)* You must go.

Down the street comes a strange looking man dressed half in red and half in yellow. He is carrying a long, thin pipe. Everyone falls silent and watches him.

Pied Piper: *(quietly)* I can take away your rats.

Mayor: *(desperately)* You can have ten bags of gold if you can do it – no, twenty bags. When can you start?

Pied Piper: I can do it now. You promise you'll give me the money?

Mayor: Yes! Yes! Twenty bags of gold. We promise.

The piper raises his pipe to his lips and starts to play softly.
Rats scuttle out of every corner. They like the magical tune.
The piper walks off down the street towards the river.
The rats follow him. There are thousands of them.

Women with brushes: Hooray! All the rats are following.

Man with hat: Look! They're running into the water.
They're going to drown!

All: Hooray! Hooray! We will be rid of the rats for ever!

People dance with joy. They shake hands with the Mayor
and pat him on the back.

Cook: Three cheers for the Mayor.

hooray for the piper

As the crowd cheers, the piper returns. Everyone turns to watch him.

Pied Piper: Please can I have my money?

Mayor: Money? *(laughing)* What money?

Pied Piper: My twenty bags of gold.

Mayor: You must be joking. You'd better leave before we set our dogs on you.

Pied Piper: *(softly)* You promised.

Mayor: Did any of you hear me promise?

Woman with basket: *(laughing)* I heard nothing.

Man with hat: *(laughing)* I heard nothing.

Cook: *(laughing)* I heard nothing.

Women with brushes: Go on – go away or we'll hit you with our brushes.

Mayor: Yes. Go away. We don't want your sort here.

Pied Piper: *(lifting his pipe)* A promise is a promise and a broken promise must be paid for.

Everyone laughs and makes fun of the piper who begins to play his pipe. The tune is different and lively. As he walks away, all the town's children stop what they are doing and follow him. The adults are helpless. They seem unable to move. They watch, horrified, as their children follow the piper.

Woman with basket: He's going to drown them in the river.

Man with hat: No, they're crossing over the bridge.

Woman with baby: Look, they're climbing the hill.

Cook: *(in astonishment)* I can't believe it. The hillside has opened – they're going inside! Now it's closed again.
(To the Mayor) Where have they gone?

Mayor: How should I know?

Women with brushes: *(angrily)* But it's your fault. You have lost our children. You broke your promise – you should have paid the piper.

Everyone turns on the Mayor and starts blaming him.

Man with hat: Wait! We are to blame as well. We laughed at the piper and we wouldn't give him his money. We broke our promise. We have paid a terrible price – we have lost our children.

Lame Boy: *(enters)* I was too slow. When the hillside opened, I saw a beautiful valley but before I could go into it, the hillside closed again. Now I'll have no-one to play with. All my friends have gone for ever.

Woman with basket: *(solemnly, putting her arm around the lame boy)* We've learned our lesson. Let's warn people what happens when you break a promise.

Cook: But what can we do?

Man with hat: We'll put up a notice that tells the story of what happened to us.

Woman with baby: *(as people begin to write the notice)* Then people will read our story and tell it to their children, who, in years to come, will tell it to their children too. And so our broken promise will be remembered – for evermore.

Everyone looks at the Mayor. They watch as the man with the hat fixes the notice onto the wall. Then, one by one, they walk away. Finally only the Mayor is left sitting in front of the notice with his head in his hands.